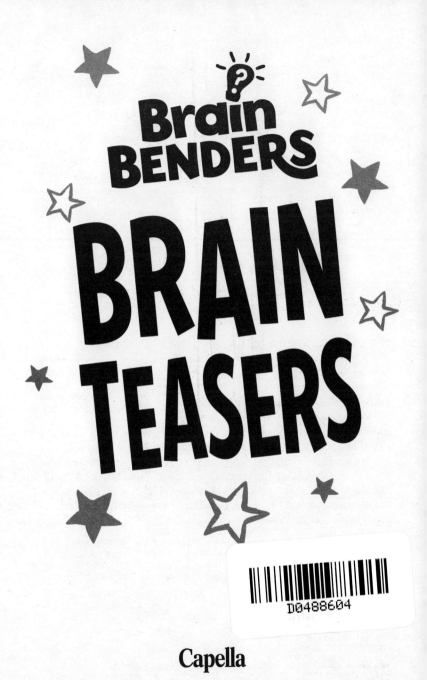

Brain BENDERS

BRAIN TEASERS

Capella

This edition published in 2020 by Arcturus Publishing Limited
26/27 Bickels Yard, 151–153 Bermondsey Street,
London SE1 3HA

ISBN: 978-1-78828-061-7
CH005923NT
Supplier 10, Date 1020, Print run 10864

Illustrated by Andy Peters

Printed in the UK

MIX
Paper from
responsible sources
FSC® C018072

CONTENTS

EYE TRICKS

Cubing It

Are the black shapes at the top or the bottom of the cubes? Look closely, and you'll see them both ways.

Crazy Cat

This cat looks like it's sitting on a normal staircase. But can you discover how it got up there? The stairs are actually impossible to climb!

Impossible Shelves

How many shelves can you see? Are you sure about the number? Count them again. Depending on how you look at the picture, you may see three shelves or four.

Sausage Finger Trick

Follow the steps to create your own incredible trick of the eye. Get your friends to try it, too!

1 Place your two index fingers together, and bring them level with your face, so they're touching the tip of your nose.

2 Now move your fingers away from your nose slowly while looking past them. A floating sausage will appear in front of your eyes.

7

Perfect Circle?

Does this circle look wonky to you? Try tracing over it with a compass. You'll see that it's perfectly round. The lines behind the circle are making it seem bent out of shape.

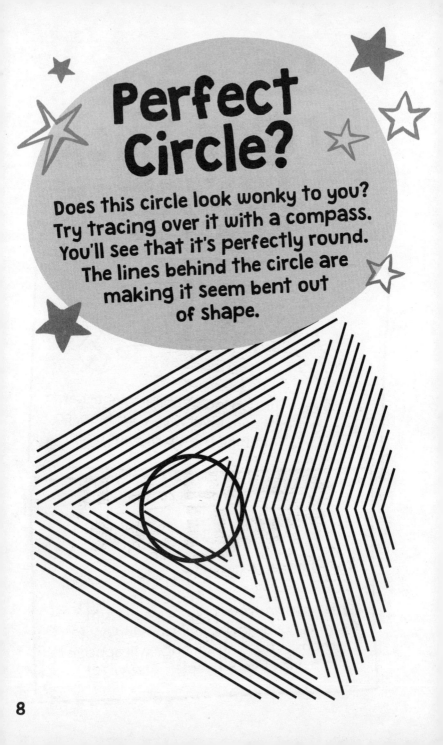

Switch On the Light

You'll need a sheet of white paper for this trick. Stare at the light bulb for 30 seconds, then look at the paper. You'll turn on the light, and the bulb will glow white!

9

Balancing Act

Is the balancing block level with the block underneath? Measure the gap between them in two places. Even though they don't look it, the two blocks are parallel to each other.

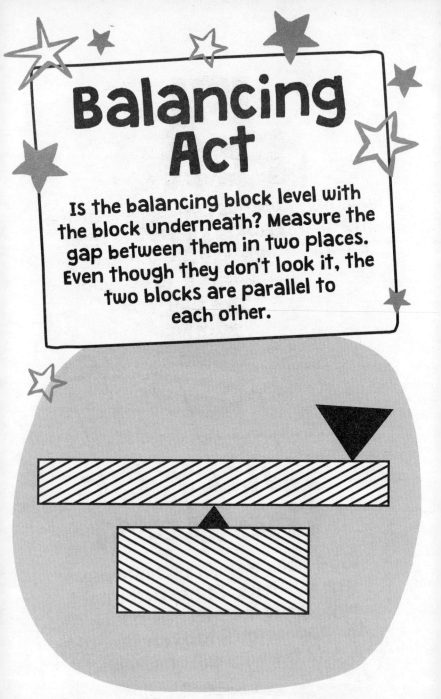

Funny Fork

How many prongs can you see at the end of this fork? It looks like three, but the prongs don't make sense. You wouldn't be able to eat your dinner with a funny fork like this!

Crazy Train Tracks

A train would have a hard time moving along these tracks. Or would it? Even though these lines don't look parallel, they are. The crossing lines make them bend.

Animal Magic

These magical animals can transform themselves. What do you see? A swan or a squirrel? A donkey or a seal?

Never-Ending Steps

Try climbing these steps. Can you reach the top? If you can, what has happened to the bottom step? A person who really climbed these steps would be climbing forever.

Hole in Your Hand

Confuse your eyes, and make a hole magically appear in your hand!

1 Take a piece of paper, and roll it into a tube.

2 Hold the tube up to one eye while you cover your other eye with your free hand.

3 Keep both eyes open, and slowly move your free hand away from your face along the edge of the tube. A hole will appear in your hand.

Why does this happen?

The hole appears because, although your eyes see two different pictures, your brain tries to make sense of them and turns them into one picture.

IDENTICAL PAIRS

Cool Headgear

These baseball caps look the same, but are they? Only two are identical. Figure out which two.

Crazy Chameleons

Which two crazy chameleons lounging on the branches are identical?

Pack Your Sack

Two of these rucksacks are the same. Can you find out which two?

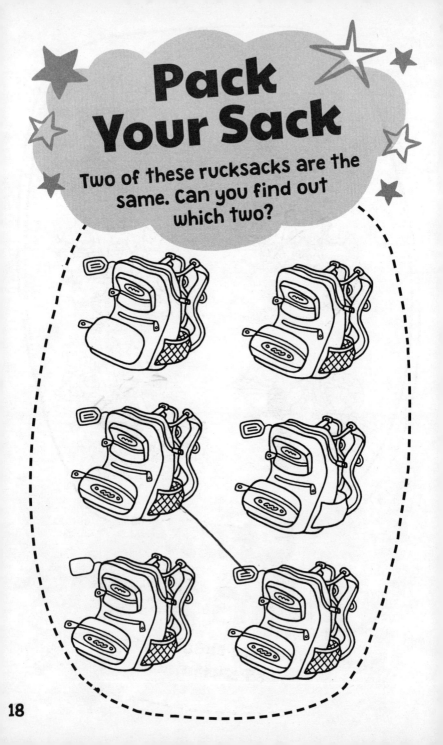

Panda Snack

Which two of these munching pandas are exactly the same as each other?

Fantastic Fruit

can you spot which two juicy fruit boxes are identical?

Snap to It

These snapping crocodiles look the same, but are they? Only two match. Find out which two.

Which Honey Jars?

Which two jars filled to the brim with yummy honey are the same?

Woof-Woof!

Take a look at these funny spotted dogs. Which two are identical?

Yee-Haw Hat!

These cowgirl hats look identical, but they're not. Only two are the same. Can you spot which two?

Fabulous Fish

Which two fabulous fish are the same as each other? Look closely to find out.

Robot Dog

Take a look at these cute robot dogs. Figure out which two are the same.

Weedy Seahorse

Two of these seahorses clinging to their seaweed are identical. Can you tell which two?

Whooooooh!

Two of these spooky spirits are the same. Can you discover which two?

Pick a Penguin

Which two penguins sheltering their eggs are identical?

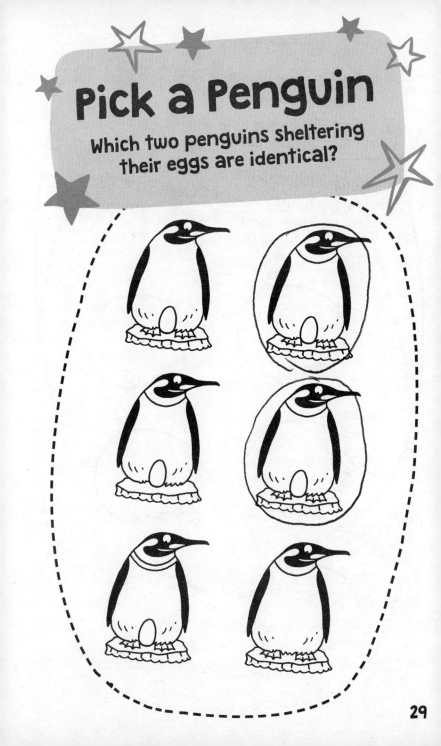

Dazzling Bangle

These beaded bangles look similar, but only two of them match. Decide which two they are.

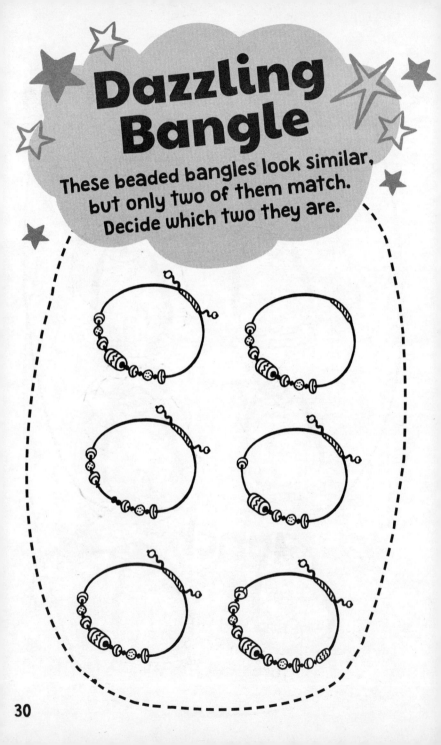

Munch-Munch!

These munching mini beetles are enjoying their feast. Which two pictures are the same?

Rolling Along

These hi-tech Rollerblades will have you whizzing down the road. Which two pictures are identical?

Sunbather

This sunbather has left behind her towel and shades. Which two pictures are the same?

Hungry Chicks

The hungry chicks are calling from their nest. Can you spot which two nests are the same?

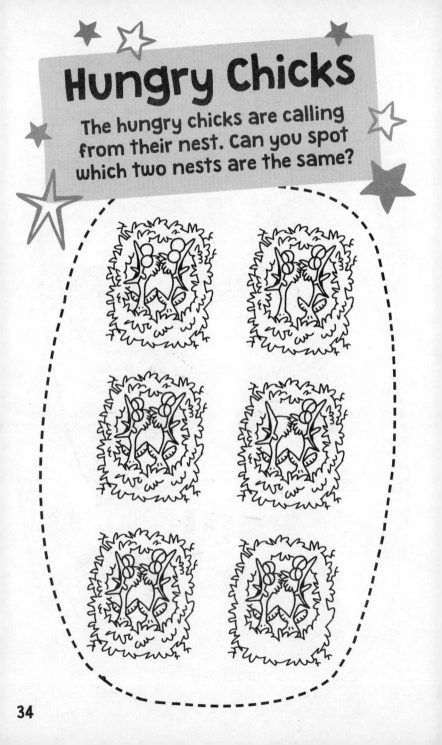

Lacy Butterflies

Two of these lacy butterflies are identical. Figure out which two they are.

PUT YOUR MIND TO IT

US
CURY
URA
OID
MER
NEP
RS
VEN
EA
TUNE
RTH
NUS
MA
TO
JUP
ASTER
MO
ON
SAT
ITER
PLU
URN

Planet Disaster

Oh no! The planets in our solar system have collided and broken apart. Match the word parts to put them back together. What three other space objects did you find?

Matchstick Squares

Try this tricky teaser. Change the four squares shown here into five squares by moving two matchsticks only.

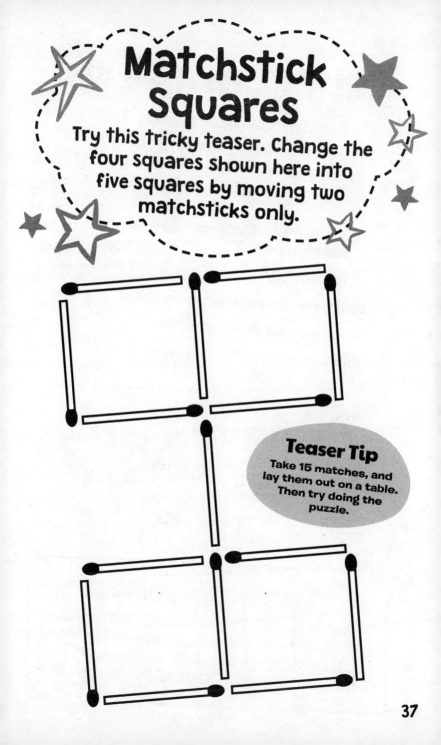

Teaser Tip
Take 15 matches, and lay them out on a table. Then try doing the puzzle.

Cool Camping

Louis is going camping this weekend. Can you work out how many of his friends are coming with him?

★ It's more than 3 but fewer than 20.

★ It's not 10.

★ It's not an odd number.

★ It can't be divided by 3.

★ It's not a multiple of 4.

Teaser Tip

Write down all the numbers from 1 to 20, then cross them out as you figure out the clues.

All Squared Up

How many squares can you count? Think carefully!

What's the Word?

Read the sign. Can you spot what's wrong with the phrase? If you can't, try again, and look at each word separately.

A
BIRD
IN (THE)
THE BUSH

Cute Cat Story

Once a Siamese cat named Nelly lived in a house. There were three other cats in the house. Their names were Bertie, Bingo, and Margot. What do you think the fourth cat's name was?

Magic Square

(Bronze)

People have been amazed by magic squares since ancient times. In a magic square, the numbers in each row, column, and diagonal always add up to the same number. Can you complete this magic square? Follow the instructions below. Good luck!

Teaser Tip
Write down the numbers from 1 to 9 on a separate sheet of paper, and cross them off as you put them on the grid.

★ Write the numbers 1 to 9 in the grid.

★ Use each number only once.

★ Each row, column, and diagonal must add up to 15.

6		8
2		

Letter Ladders

Make your way down the ladders by changing only one letter in the word above to make a new word. If you get stuck or end up with too many words, you can use the clues to help, but try doing it without them first!

Teaser Tip

Look for letters that appear at both the top and the bottom of the ladder. Your words will always contain them.

M I L K	
S I L K	
S U L K	
B U L K	

Clues

★ This is a type of soft material.

★ People in a bad mood do this.

Clues

★ When you can't find something, it is ...

★ You're at the back of the pack.

L O S E
L O S T
L A S T
F A S T

41

Mental Mind-Reading Trick

Try out this incredible number trick on yourself. We guarantee you will be amazed!

1 Pick a number between 1 and 10.

2 Multiply the number by 9.

3 Add the digits of the number you made in step two together.

4 Subtract 5 from the new number.

5 Find a letter in the alphabet that matches the number you made in step four, e.g. 1 = A, 2 = B, etc.

6 Pick a country that starts with that letter.

7 Choose an animal that starts with the last letter of your country.

8 Pick a shade that starts with the last letter of your animal.

9 What's your answer? Now turn to page 114.

Teaser Tip

Try this trick on your friends. Tell them you're a mind reader, and give them the answer!

Pieces of Pie

Can you discover which number is missing from the last piece of pie?

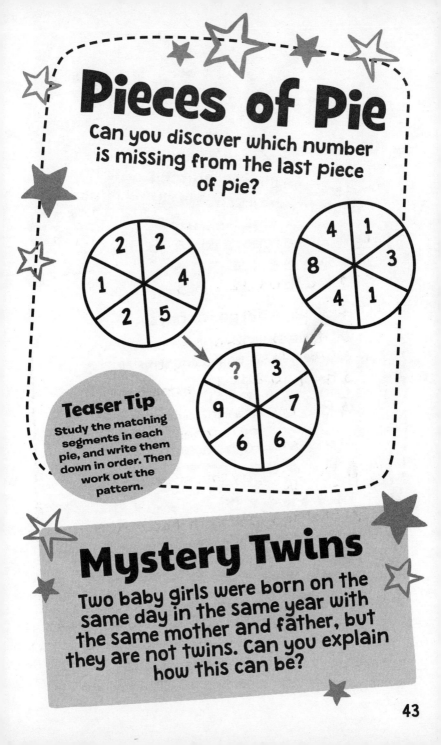

2 2
1 4
2 5

4 1
8 3
4 1

? 3
9 7
6 6

Teaser Tip

Study the matching segments in each pie, and write them down in order. Then work out the pattern.

Mystery Twins

Two baby girls were born on the same day in the same year with the same mother and father, but they are not twins. Can you explain how this can be?

It's No Joke!

Use the code buster to figure out the answers to these jokes, and have a good chuckle.

Q: What's a robot's top food choice?

A: ✦ ♣ ◆ ■ ♣ ◆ ★ ♣ □ ❖
   M I C R O C H I P S

Q: How can a girl go for days without sleep?

A: ❖ ★ ♥   ♣ ✳ ▼ ❀   ❖ ▼ ♥ ♥ □ ❖
   S H E   O N L Y   S L E E P S

   ◐ ○   ✳ ♣ ❀ ★ ○
   A T   N I G H T

Q: Why was the crab arrested?

A: ★ ♥   ▶ ✪ ❖   ✪ ▼ ♥ ▶ ✪   ❀ ❖
   H E   W A S   A L W A Y S

   □ ♣ ✳ ◆ ★ ♣ ✳ ❀   ○ ★ ✳ ❀ ✪ ❖
   P I N C H I N G   T H I N G S

Code Buster

A	B	C	D	E	F	G	H	I	J	K	L	M
✪	✳	◆	☆	♥	☆	❀	★	♣	▲	✖	▼	✦

N	O	P	Q	R	S	T	U	V	W	X	Y	Z
✳	♣	□	✓	■	❖	○	✳	✳	▶	▶	❀	✧

44

Matchstick Triangles

Bend your brain around this puzzle. Change the nine equal triangles shown here into five triangles by removing five matchsticks.

Teaser Tip

Try this puzzle with real sticks, and experiment with different positions.

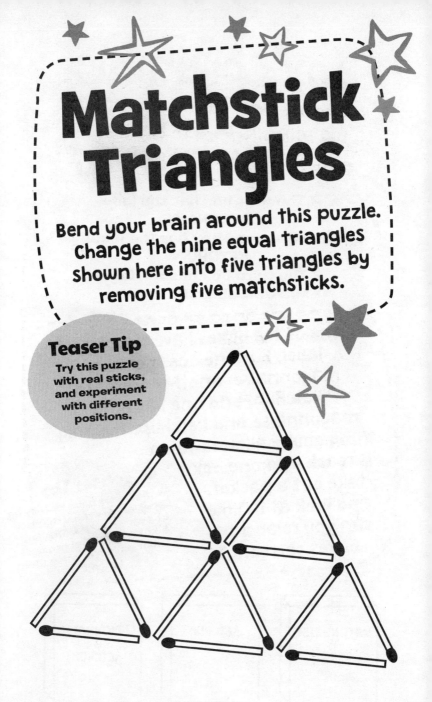

Box Scramble

You've been asked to help sort out a big mix-up. In front of you are three boxes.

★ The first box has the label **MAYONNAISE**.
★ The second box has the label **KETCHUP**.
★ The third box has the label **MAYONNAISE & KETCHUP**.

None of the boxes have the correct label, but one does contain mayonnaise, another contains ketchup, and one has both mayonnaise and ketchup. The only thing you're allowed to do is reach into one box, take out a packet, and look at it. How can you relabel the boxes correctly?

Teaser Tip

All the boxes have the wrong label, so you know that the box with the "MAYONNAISE & KETCHUP" label can only contain mayonnaise OR ketchup.

| MAYONNAISE | KETCHUP | MAYONNAISE & KETCHUP |

Magic Square (Silver)

Did you manage to complete the magic square on page 40? If so, it's time to up the stakes!

★ Write the numbers 1 to 16 in the grid.

★ Use each number only once.

★ Each row, column, and diagonal must add up to 34.

Teaser Tip
Tackle the rows, columns, or diagonals with the most numbers in them first.

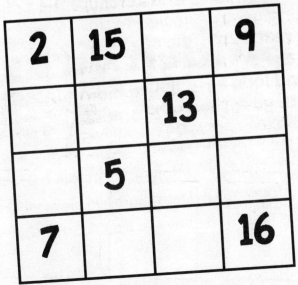

2	15		9
		13	
	5		
7			16

Mixed-Up Tags

Unscramble the letters to discover what musical gifts are attached to the tags.

drum kit

rudm tki

mopircohen

sorkeyabd

dehanophes

pesakres

guitar

tugrai

Hidden Birds

Can you find a bird hiding in each of these sentences?

Jane was speaking French awkwardly.

The flea gleefully jumped on the cat.

There was a painful throb in his arm.

"How long do we have to wait for the bus?" she asked.

Clever Coins

Try to solve this tricky puzzle with coins and then challenge your friends to work out the solution!

First, find 5 coins. You will need 3 copper and 2 silver coins.

Arrange them in this pattern:

Now, try to make this pattern:

The rules are:

1. You can make only 3 moves
2. You must move 2 coins next to each other at a time.

Can you do it?

They're Bugging Me!

The bugs are all on the loose! Match the word parts together to find the name of 12 creepy critters.

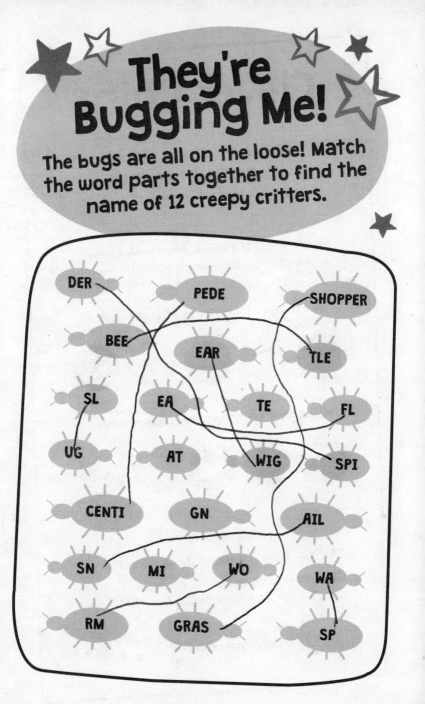

DER

PEDE

SHOPPER

BEE

EAR

TLE

SL

EA

TE

FL

UG

AT

WIG

SPI

CENTI

GN

AIL

SN

MI

WO

WA

RM

GRAS

SP

Got the Wrong Number?

Which number shouldn't be in each of these stars?

Teaser Tip
Look for a pattern in each star, and then see which number doesn't fit.

A
7
11 23 13
17 9
31 22

B
12
24 18 10
36 30
48 6

Loopy Group

A group of kids are standing in a row. Work out the fewest number of kids there can be in the row.

A girl is to the left of a boy.

A boy is to the left of a boy.

Two boys are to the right of a girl.

Teaser Tip
Draw a diagram. The answer is not 4.

Brick by Brick

Jeremy and Mike can build a wall 5 bricks long and 5 bricks high in 1 minute. How long will it take them to build a wall 10 bricks long and 10 bricks high?

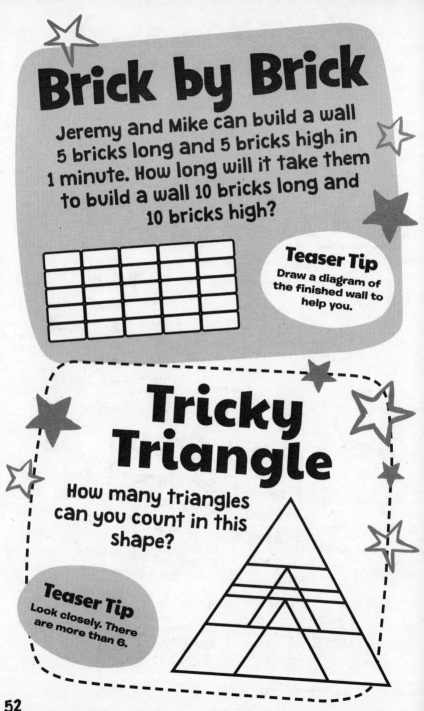

Teaser Tip
Draw a diagram of the finished wall to help you.

Tricky Triangle

How many triangles can you count in this shape?

Teaser Tip
Look closely. There are more than 6.

Magic Square (Gold)

Go for broke, and try to complete this very hard magic square!

★ Write the numbers 1 to 24 in the grid.

★ Use each number only once.

★ Each row, column, and diagonal must add up to 65.

Teaser Tip
Check your answers when you complete a row or column. Write down the different addition combinations.

25	16			
1		20	17	21
	22	14		7
	13	12	23	2

53

Mystery Creature

Cross out the letters that appear more than once. Then unscramble the leftover letters to discover a legendary creature.

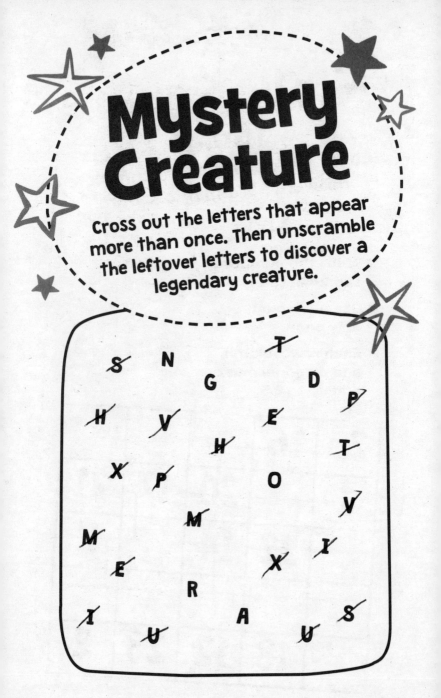

Puzzling Pyramid

Every number on the upper level of the pyramid is the total of the two numbers below it, e.g. 11 + 7 = 18. Can you climb to the top?

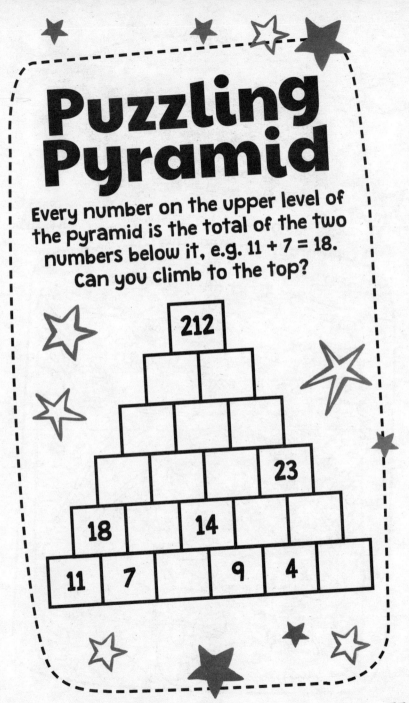

SPOT THE DIFFERENCE

Whizzing Along

It's crowded out on the ski slopes today! Can you can spot eight differences between the two pictures?

Wacky Museum Tour

Take a tour around this wonderfully weird museum of past times. Look for eight differences between the two pictures.

Inventor at Work

This scientist's lab is packed with all kinds of crazy gadgets. Find eight differences between the two pictures.

Polar Adventure

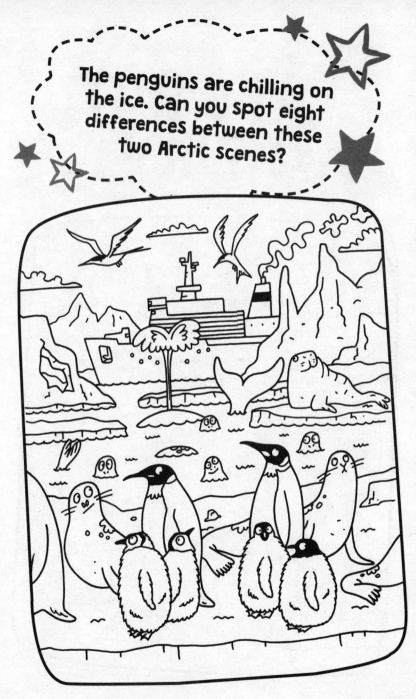

Let's Get Moving

Everyone is outdoors getting active in the park. Find eight differences between the two scenes.

Bedroom Glitz

This cowgirl's bedroom is full of glitz and glamour. Find eight differences between the two pictures.

Watery World

Dive into this underwater scene, and see if you can find eight differences between the two pictures.

Jungle Party

The animals are having lots of fun hanging out in the forest. Look for eight differences between the two scenes.

Spooky Graveyard

Boo! Find eight differences between the two spooky graveyards ... if you dare.

Alien Planet

The bouncing astronaut has some aliens to keep him company! Find eight differences between the two scenes.

SHADOW MATCH

Monkey Magic

Look closely at the curly-tailed monkey. Only one shadow matches it. Which one is it?

Majestic Castle

Which shadow matches the picture of the majestic medieval castle?

Funky Guitar

Find the shadow that matches the funky guitar. Then play yourself a crazy solo!

Sneaky salamander

Which shadow matches the salamander sneaking across the page?

Beautiful Blooms

Look closely at the lovely flowers. Only one shadow matches the picture exactly. Which one is it?

Fiery Dragon

Which shadow matches the picture of the fire-breathing dragon?

Moose On The Loose

Uh-oh! There's a wild moose on the loose. Find the shadow that matches it.

Magical Lamp

Here's a shiny magic lamp to rub and make a wish. Which shadow matches it exactly?

Which Keys?

Look closely at the bunch of keys. Only one shadow matches the picture. Which one is it?

Take a Bite

Quick, get out of the water! Which shadow matches the ferocious shark?

Palm Beach

Find the shadow that matches the desert island. Then snooze a while under the palm tree!

Tou-Can Do It!

Only one of these shadows matches the toucan sitting on a branch. Which one is it?

Moth Match

Which shadow is the same as the patterned moth fluttering across the page?

Skydiving

This daredevil man has parachuted from the sky! Which shadow matches him exactly?

Precious Stones

Look closely at the pretty necklace. Only one shadow is the same. Which one is it?

Spiky Stegosaurus

Which shadow matches the picture of the spiky Stegosaurus?

Prickly Pear

Ouch! Watch out for that prickly pear in the pot. Which shadow matches it exactly?

Boing, Boing!

Can you spot the shadow that matches the bouncing kangaroo?

Flying High

Look closely at the kite in the sky.
Only one shadow is the same.
Which one is it?

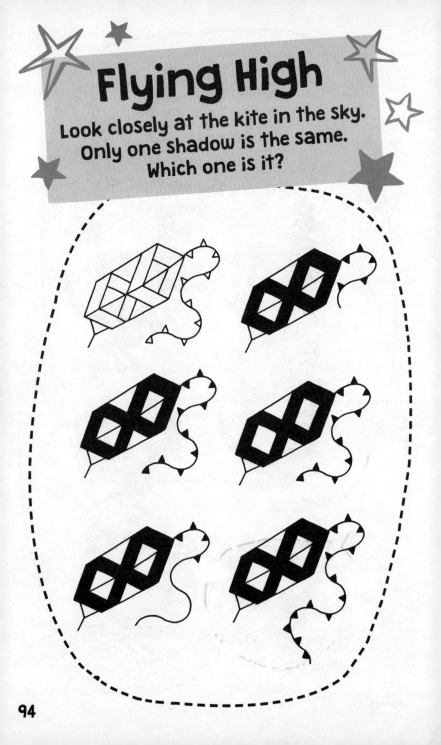

Pampered Pooch

This pretty poodle is ready for the dog show! Which shadow matches it exactly?

MORE EYE TRICKS

Moving Pattern Art

Try staring at the middle of this image. It should look as if it's pulsating.

The Hills Are Alive

Let your eyes follow the ripples from the outer edge toward the middle. Can you see the pattern form a small hill?

Serious Spiral?

Does this look like a spiral to you? Try following the rings with your finger. You'll find they're actually concentric circles with the same central point.

Vicious Circles

This scary pattern is just a group of short lines. Its "teeth" trick your eyes into seeing a spiral.

Twisted Circles

Trace these circles with a compass, and you'll find they're perfectly round. The confusing background pattern makes them appear distorted.

Seeing Stars

Gaze at the black stars under a bright light. After a little while, you should see white stars bouncing in between them.

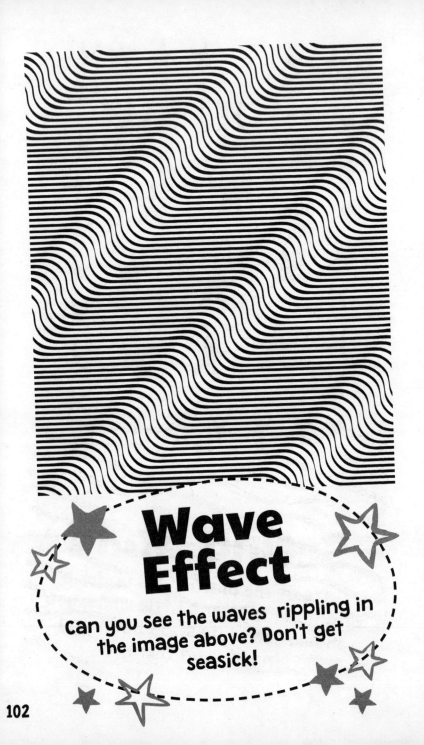

Wave Effect

Can you see the waves rippling in the image above? Don't get seasick!

Rolling Tide

Slide your eyes over this illusion, and watch the waves twist and roll.

Inside Out

Is this illusion a cone coming toward you or a tunnel going away from you?

Outside In

Is this illusion a tunnel going away from you or a cone coming toward you?

Multimix

What do you see when you look at this image? Is it a pattern of circles, triangles, or curve-sided stars?

Answers

IDENTICAL PAIRS

Page 16

Page 17

Page 18

Page 19

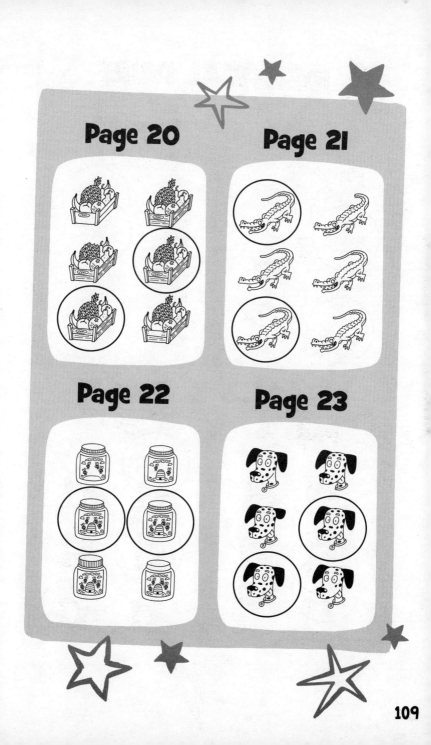

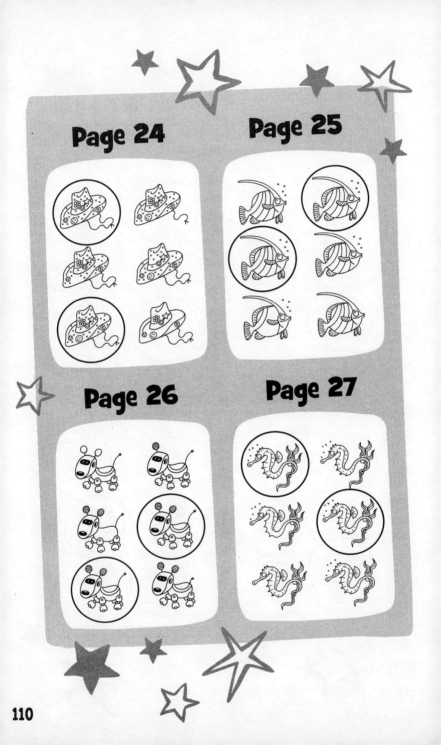

Page 24

Page 25

Page 26

Page 27

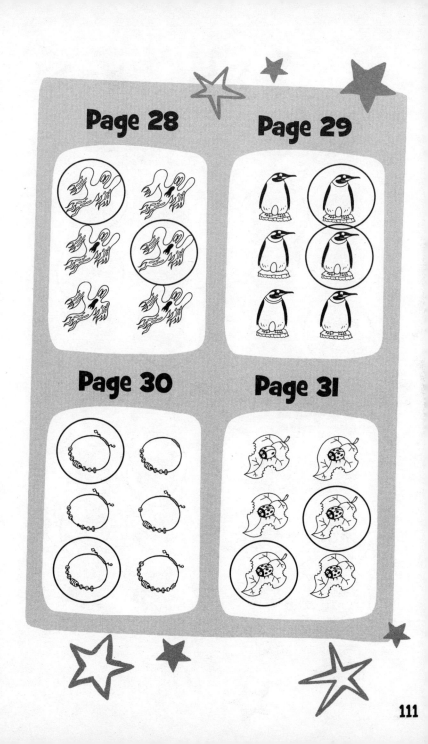

Page 32

Page 33

Page 34

Page 35

PUT YOUR MIND TO IT

Page 36 Planet Disaster

The planets are:

Mercury	Venus	Earth	Mars
Jupiter	Saturn	Uranus	Neptune

The other three space objects are an asteroid, the dwarf planet Pluto, and the Moon.

Page 37 Matchstick Squares

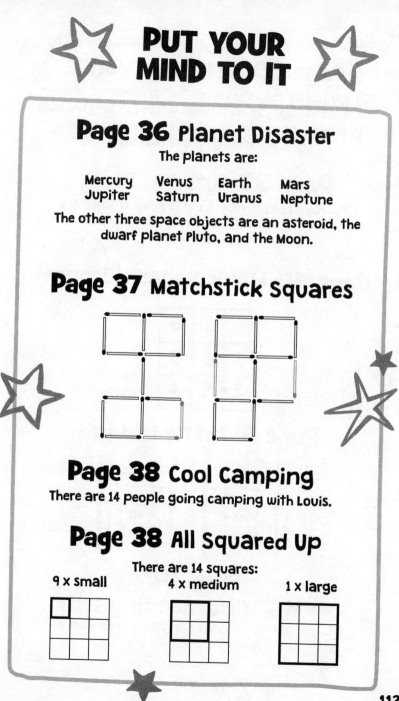

Page 38 Cool Camping

There are 14 people going camping with Louis.

Page 38 All Squared Up

There are 14 squares:

9 x small   4 x medium   1 x large

Page 39 What's the Word?

Did you notice that the word "the" is repeated twice in the sign? It's easy to miss when you're reading because your eyes jump over words. But if you look at each word separately, you should see it.

Page 39 Cute Cat Story

The name of the fourth cat is Nelly. If there are three other cats in the house, then she must be the fourth cat!

Page 40 Magic Square (Bronze)

6	1	8
7	5	3
2	9	4

Page 41 Letter Ladders

MILK
SILK
SULK
BULK

LOSE
LOST
LAST
FAST

Page 42
Mental Mind-Reading Trick

Did you get "an orange kangaroo in Denmark"? Almost everyone does!

Page 43 Pieces of Pie

The missing number is 6. The number in the third piece of pie is the total of the two numbers in the other matching pieces, so 2 + 4 = 6.

Page 43 Mystery Twins

The two baby girls are from a set of triplets.

Page 44 It's No Joke!

The answers to the jokes are:

Q: What's a robot's top food choice?
A: Microchips.

Q: How can a girl go for days without sleep?
A: She only sleeps at night.

Q: Why was the crab arrested?
A: He was caught pinching things.

Page 45 Matchstick Triangles

Page 46 Box Scramble

Here's what to do to relabel the boxes correctly:

Look inside the box with the MAYONNAISE & KETCHUP label. You know this label is wrong, so if you pull out a ketchup packet, it must be the ketchup box.

The box with the MAYONNAISE label cannot contain mayonnaise because it has the wrong label. It can't contain ketchup, either, because you've used that label, so it must contain mayonnaise and ketchup.

The final box, KETCHUP, also has the wrong label, so it can't contain ketchup. It must contain mayonnaise because that's the only free label left.

Page 47 Magic Square (Silver)

2	15	8	9
14	4	13	3
11	5	12	6
7	10	1	16

Page 48 Mixed-Up Tags

Drum kit, microphone, keyboards, headphones, speakers, guitar.

Page 48 Hidden Birds

Jane was speaking Frenc**h awk**wardly.
The fl**ea gle**efully jumped on the cat.
There was a painful th**rob in** his arm.
"H**ow l**ong do we have to wait for the bus?" she asked.

Page 49 Clever Coins

The three moves are:

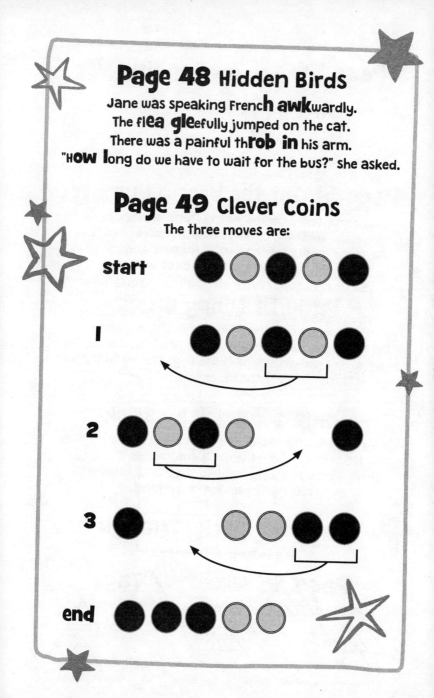

start

1

2

3

end

Page 50 They're Bugging Me!

The bugs are:

Beetle   Grasshopper   Centipede
Gnat   Snail   Earwig
Flea   Wasp   Worm
Slug   Spider   Mite

Page 51 Got the Wrong Number?

A: 22 is the wrong number.
All the others are odd numbers.
B: 10 is the wrong number.
All the others are multiples of 6.

Page 51 Loopy Group

The fewest number of kids is 3: girl, boy, boy.
The answer is not 4 because there are two boys to the
right of the girl, so one of those boys can be to the left
of the other boy.

Page 52 Brick by Brick

A 5 x 5 brick wall has 25 bricks, but a 10 x 10 brick wall
has 100 bricks. That's 4 times as many. So, it will take
them 4 times as long to build the 10 x 10 brick wall,
making the answer 4 minutes.

Page 52 Tricky Triangle

The total is 10 triangles.

118

Page 53
Magic Square (Gold)

25	16	9	4	11
1	6	20	17	21
19	22	14	3	7
5	8	10	18	24
15	13	12	23	2

Page 54 Mystery Creature
The answer is a dragon.

Page 55 Puzzling Pyramid

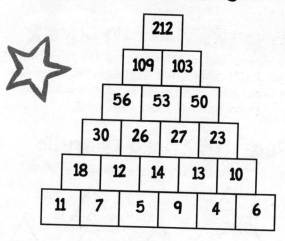

SPOT THE DIFFERENCE

Page 56

Page 58

Page 60

Page 62

Page 64

Page 66

Page 68

Page 70

Page 72

Page 74

SHADOW MATCH

Page 76

Page 77

Page 78

Page 79

Page 80

Page 81

Page 86

Page 87

Page 88

Page 89

125

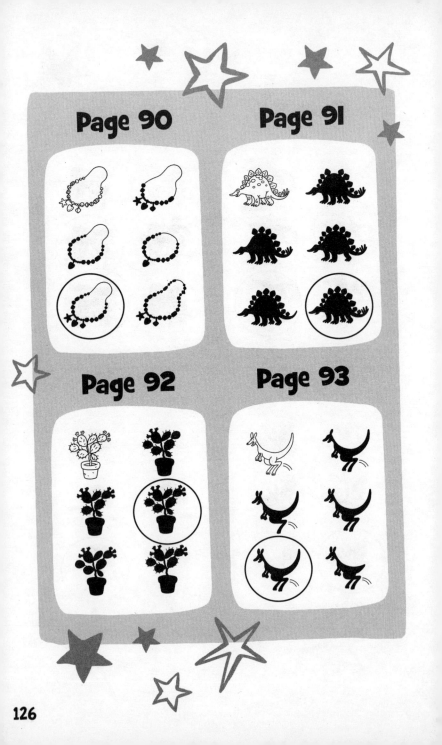

Page 90

Page 91

Page 92

Page 93

126

Page 94

Page 95